THE BEST OF
HERMAN
1

"Two round-the-world cruises
in opposite directions."

GRUB STREET LONDON

Published by Grub Street
The Basement, 10 Chivalry Road
London SW11 1HT

Copyright © 1990 by Universal Press Syndicate

British Library Cataloguing in Publication Data
Unger, Jim
The best of Herman.
Vol. 1
1. American humorous cartoons
I. Title
741.5973

ISBN 0-948817-38-0

Printed and bound in Great Britain by Clays Ltd

"It's coming."

"The dog wants to come in."

**"I don't think I can read any of it.
You're holding it too close."**

**"OK! Now stay exactly like that and I'll
move the chart over to the other wall."**

"I'd hazard a guess there's an 'E' on there somewhere."

"They may need a minor adjustment."

**"There are some gentlemen here
to fix the copy machine."**

"Today's topic is 'public awareness.'"

"I always wear my lucky
hat for job interviews."

"I like a man who knows
where he's going."

"Your resume says you
spent 'fore years at collej.'"

"*You're* a vet. Don't *you* know what it is?"

"Don't ask."

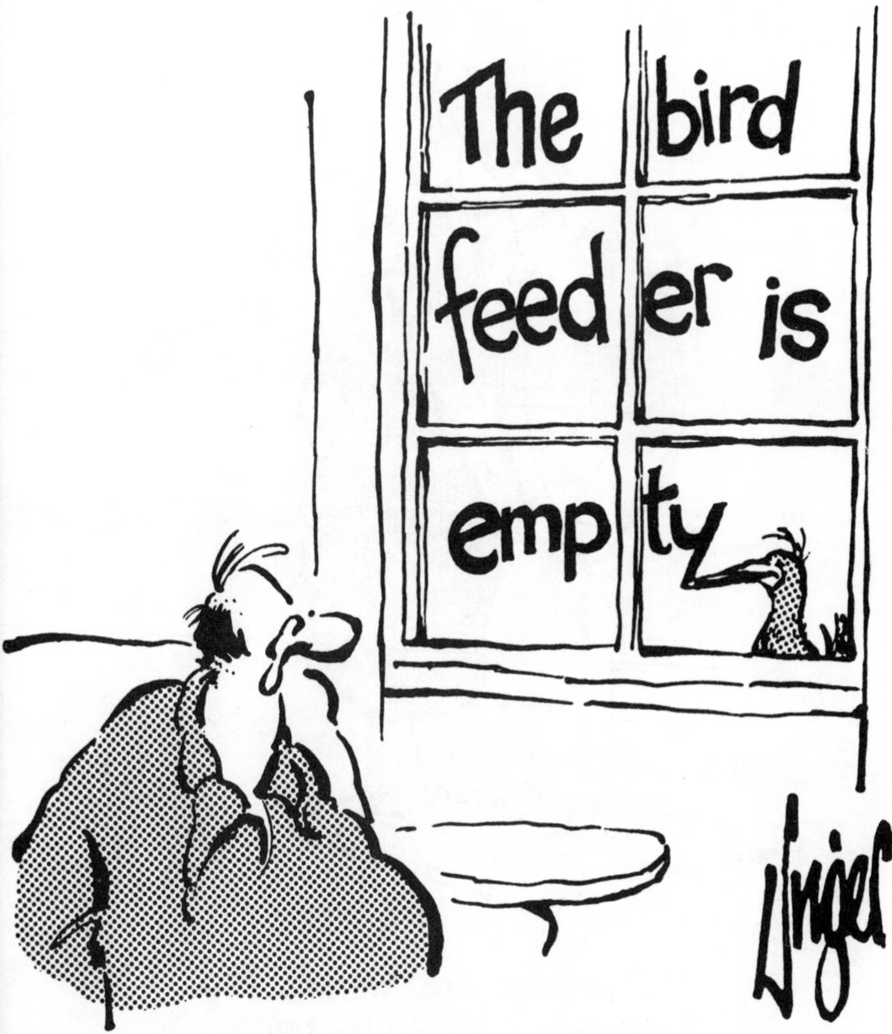
The bird feeder is empty
Unger

"There we are. What's 350 pounds divided by two?"

"How do you say, 'We came to your country to find our suitcases'?"

"There're only two of these
left in the entire world."

"Did you see which way
the camel went?"

"Don't keep shouting 'call the plumber.' I've called the plumber."

"It's a whole different world down there."

"What happened to the picture?"

**"I'm sorry, sir, you can't
come in without a jacket."**

"I'll take over, Wilson."

"Will you please take this thing away
from him. I'm *trying* to read."

"There's just no pleasing you,
is there? All week you've been
telling me to get a haircut."

"How d'you expect me to do all
this homework without a computer?"

"You say you've got a
ringing in your ears...."

"I'd like to borrow just enough to get myself out of debt."

"I need a door like this but with number 37 on it. ... We're moving."

"We handle hi-fi stereo, sir.
You need a blacksmith."

"I know I'm not supposed to interfere, but how's the dog going to climb through that?"

"Why don't you listen? I said, 'Send over a *can* of glue.'"

"I thought you were
going to mow the lawn."

"Thanks for a lovely party last night.
I know George had a good time."

"There's one that needs trimming."

"I'm not interested in excuses,
Mildew. You're four minutes late."

"Don't tell me. Let me guess."

"He says there's definitely no intelligent life down here."

"OK, five more minutes, then we'll go somewhere else."

**"Mother, I thought we'd agreed
. . . 'no luxuries.'"**

"I won't be able to eat all of this. Do you want the cherry?"

**"Six years ago he started
putting up a towel rack."**

"He never did have a lot of patience."

"It's still wobbling."

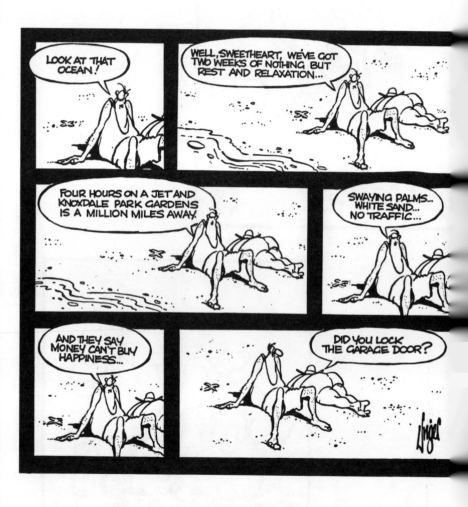

"I'm second from the left, back row."

"Any luck?"

"Say when."

"We didn't have any ice, so I put a piece of frozen pizza in it."

"There's nothing on TV. D'you
want to have an argument?"

"Couldn't you hear me knocking?"

"What's the fish like today?"

**"Would you like to donate something
to the charity of your choice?"**

"You name it. I'm collecting for it."

"OK. OK. *Not* guilty."

"You expect me to tell the truth,
the whole truth, and nothing but
the truth, and then you ask
me a question like that!"

"Let's get out of here."

"Table for 650."

"I wanna try something. Grab
both my legs and push."

"OK. I'll be back to pick you
up in 25 years. What time?"

"I told your boss you were
going camping for 12 years."

"You're being released. Be ready
to leave in 30 minutes."

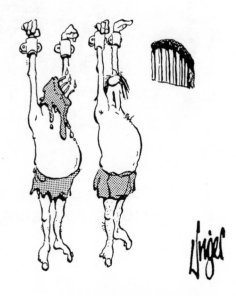

"You shouldn't have told
him it was your birthday."

"You need a haircut. It's touching your shoulders."

"It's a Siberian mountain dog."

"Joyce, how much do I charge
people when I don't know
what's wrong with them?"

"You don't have to keep
smiling for a chest X-ray."

"They found your other ski."

"Here's my bill. That should stop you from smoking and drinking for a few months."

"D'you want me to pull it off fast or slow?"

"Watch out, Maurice.
It may be a trap."

"Cradle snatcher!"

"Is this No. 11?"

**"Stop me when I get to
something I can borrow."**

"Listen, I'd better go. That guy's
still waiting to get his clothes."

"Where did these bathroom scales come from?"

"You never give up, do you!"

"He's trying to talk!"

"Here, kitty, kitty."

"I would also like to thank my tropical
fish for being there when I needed them."

"I've lost the keys to my house. Can I live here?"

"What's wrong with this door?"

"Just a little exploratory surgery."

"I can't stop."

"Anyone would think you're the only person in the world who was ever stung on the nose by a bee."

"They're keeping me in for observation."

"Are you three all together?"

"I took my school report card in
to get it framed and they lost it."

**"Run out the back and stick 'Happy
Birthday' on that for me."**

"Take a tip, pal. *Never* let them know you can read."

"I'm giving the goldfish a good swim."

"Come on ... you won't get to be a
guard dog just by looking at it."

"Chest, 68."

"I'll need a full-length photograph with this loan application."

"She didn't want you to kiss her."

"What do you mean he'll need a tie to get in? This is my *wife*!"

"... to have and to hold ..."

"Is there a band in front of me?"

"Listen, I'd better go. My wife's
waiting to use the phone."

"I know diamonds are forever. What have you got for a couple of months?"

"It's our anniversary. What have you got that leaves a bad taste in the mouth?"

"Do you realize it's been 12 years since we went through the express checkout?"

"Does that hurt?"

"The car's not quite as wide as it used to be."

"Maybe I should let you drive from now on."

"I hope you don't expect me to pay for a three-minute lesson."

"Don't start looking for
your glasses at 80 mph."

"Harold, I'm phoning you from the car."

"OK, you can stop signaling now."

"How's the water?"

"The little gray bits are
non-stick frying pan."

"I'll serve your dinner as
soon as the smoke clears."

"You wouldn't believe the time I had getting this cake out of the oven!"

"Do you have any special plans for this pork chop?"

"How do you stop the beans from sliding into the toaster?"

"If you order the chili, I need
to know your next-of-kin."

"The doctor says you'll probably be in *The Guinness Book of World Records.*"

"Grab your bread roll. It's in my pocket."

"D'you wanna tip me now? Then I'll
know what sort of service to give you."

"This 'Bottled in 1835' is written in ball-point pen."

"D'you want to look at the menu?"

"Maybe you were allergic to the shellfish."

"Who am I? And what
am I doing here?"

"The airline lost my luggage again."

"You put the comics page in here.
You know he likes the editorials."

"Get down, Robert. Remember
you're an accountant."